new nomads

An exploration of wearable electronics by Philips

010 Publishers, Rotterdam 2000

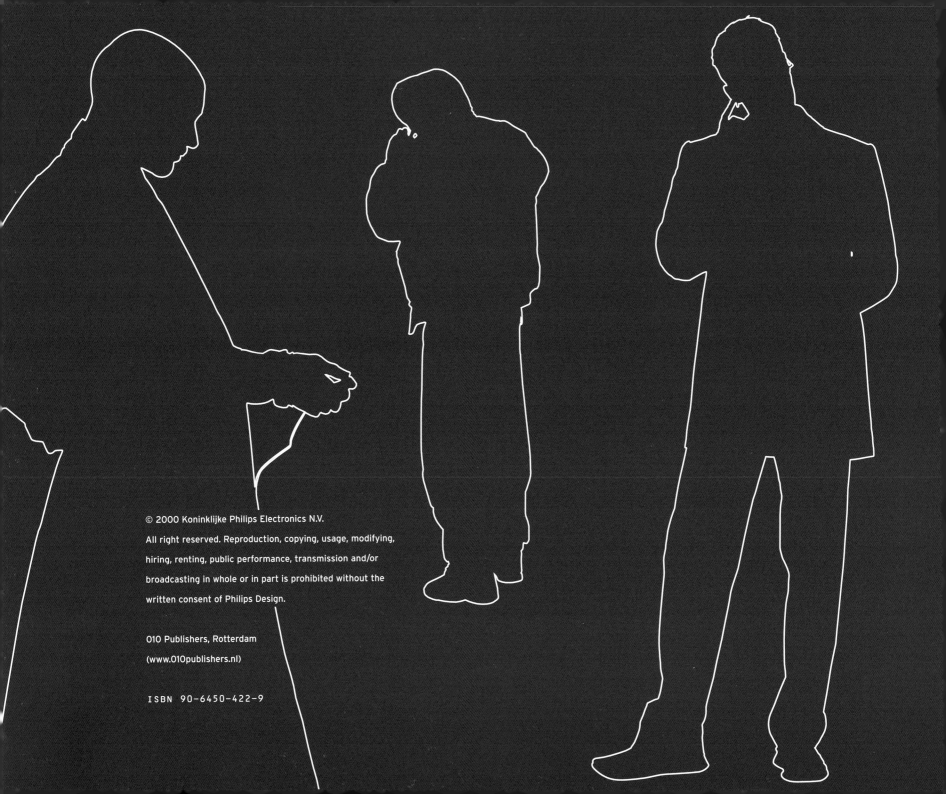

010 Publishers, Rotterdam

(www.010publishers.nl)

ISBN 90-6450-422-9

The quest for power, comfort and freedom

Stefano Marzano

The irresistible path of evolution

It is no accident that our eyes, ears, nose and fingertips are all on the outside of our bodies. As the outposts of our nervous system, their task is to gather information about the world around us and transmit it back to the brain. Our limbs carry these organs to new locations, where they can gather even more information. It is as if evolution has been governed from the start by an irresistible drive on the part of an internal life-force to explore the world beyond the mind. Now, in recent millennia, culture has taken us even further in the same direction through the development of tools. Somehow, it seems, we have, built into us, an unquenchable thirst for knowledge and experience that leads us to seek the amplification or expansion of the senses, of power, and reach.

That would seem to imply, as a logical consequence, that the ultimate goal of our species is omnipresence, omnipotence and omniscience – the ability to be everywhere, to do everything and to know everything. It is no accident that these are the characteristics we are inclined to ascribe to our gods, or to idealised creatures of our imagination, like Batman or the Bionic Woman.

The drive to become divine

To expand our powers, we have used and adapted things in our environment, finding ways outside our own physical bodies of doing all sorts of things more effectively. Take transportation. First, we were limited to using our own legs. Then we borrowed the more effective legs of horses, elephants or camels. Next, we came up with the wheel, which helped us transport objects more easily. And most recently, we have invented motor-powered devices that are even more powerful than animals: the train, the car and the aeroplane. Each time, the tool has become bigger and more complex. We have expanded our mental powers in similar ways, developing first cave painting, writing and the abacus, and eventually cameras, calculators, and computers. All these external devices are helping us towards achieving our ultimate evolutionary goal.

The principle of least effort

However, this evolution follows a course defined by the principle of least effort or least resistance. We want everything, but we want to get it with as little effort as possible. We want to do everything, but with the maximum of ease, freedom and comfort.

Product designers spend a lot of time trying to make the devices that they design easy to use. But because of the limits imposed by technology, this work can only provide ad hoc or partial solutions. What people really want is to be free of any attachments. We don't want easy tools; we don't want to bother with tools at all. Hang gliding, bungee jumping, parachuting and Harley Davidson motorbikes are all attempts to escape from the restrictions of ordinary life and to experience – even if only for short, intense moments – the feeling of ultimate freedom.

Re-interiorisation

With the present technology, we cannot yet achieve this dream. Certainly, the human race has come a long way towards its goal of liberation, but it still has far to go.

Many of the tools and products that expanded our innate powers by adding external enhancements to them were at first so big that they could not be moved. But gradually, new technologies have made it possible to miniaturise them so that we now carry them around.

This development is obvious in the case of radio and audio systems, for instance. The invention of the transistor, replacing the valve, led to a revolution in the spread of radio, taking it for the first time outside the home. The arrival of the personal stereo marked the next phase: the object is now small enough to put in your pocket. Telephones have also undergone a similar transition from static box to portable object.

Both radio and the telephone were originally an exteriorisation of our powers, extending the reach of our hearing and voice. Now, these devices are beginning to make their way back 'inside us'.

Culture and the body

This 're-interiorisation' of our expanded powers is not only liberating, it will free our lives of lots of clutter. At the moment, many 'tools' we use in the home – like televisions, video recorders and audio systems – are scattered around in the form of big black boxes. As miniaturisation continues, products will occupy less and less space and either merge invisibly into their surroundings or become objects of attention in their own right, like works of art.

So what parts of their surroundings will these technological functions ultimately merge into – and why? I suggest that it will be those objects that human beings experience as indispensable. What we feel to be indispensable derives from the physical form and nature of our bodies on the one hand, and our culture on the other. For instance, almost all cultures have things that resemble tables and chairs, even if they are only rocks or logs. All human beings take shelter in places having elements that resemble walls and roofs. And most cultures also have clothes. Different cultures may embellish them in various ways, but the basics are determined by the fact that we like to rest our bodies while still being alert, we like to do things with our hands at a certain height from the ground, and we need to protect ourselves from the elements.

All these sorts of items – tables, chairs, walls, clothes – have been around since the earliest times and are likely to be around into the distant future. Because we do not feel they are in the way, or that they are holding us back in our struggle for freedom, they are almost the ideal carriers for the functions that make us more like the gods we long to be.

Harmonising technology and fashion

But moving from miniaturisation to progressive integration calls for careful thought. Miniaturisation has changed our lives dramatically. Integration is going to change it even more. Miniaturisation has meant mainly that people have been able to perform certain operations with mobile devices; integration means that the entire relationship between people and the objects that contain embedded technology will change completely. Take clothing, for instance.

The integration of technology into clothing means the start of a new era in the fashion industry. For the first time, an industry that has traditionally been driven by style and emotional values will team up with another, totally different type of industry – the electronics industry. And for the first time, people will view clothes not only in terms of matching colours and designs but also in terms of functions.

What we are talking about here is a new lifestyle and business revolution – one that will require the electronics industry to 'think emotionally'. To guarantee human-focused solutions, we cannot expect the fashion industry to adapt itself to technology. Rather, the technology industry will have to learn how to deal with fashion.

Interaction of technology and fashion

Will the current forms taken by technology simply disappear? Will people no longer fumble with their personal stereo to change the music? And will they no longer pull a ringing mobile phone from their pocket?

Sometimes superseded objects may lose their practical function but survive in an aesthetic function. The male neck-tie, for instance, started out as a way of fastening the collar, becoming purely decorative when its function as a collar fastening was taken over by the stud. At other times, they may simply disappear. The collar stud itself, for instance, disappeared when its function was taken over by the button.

The technological functions we integrate into our clothing may similarly bring about changes in the clothing itself. Although some people may want to hide the technology away, others may want to give the new 'invisible' functions some visible form, simply in order to show other people that those functions are there. In that case, the appearance of the original object may change. Sports shoes, for instance, that began as an adaptation of conventional footwear, have now developed an aesthetic of their own, which is now spreading to affect other casual and even formal footwear. The result is that many shoes now look like sports shoes, though the people who wear them may never actually indulge in any sporting activity.

Designers may also wish to make a new function visible so that people will understand what it can do for them. Their approach is often to draw an analogy with an older function that is traditionally associated with a particular form. For instance, when electric water-heaters first came onto the market, they were made to look like the object people normally placed on the fire to heat water for drinking. Designers of software interfaces adopt this strategy all the time, with desktops, tabs, trash cans, record cards, and so on. Blending an old form with a new function in this way makes it easier for people to understand and accept new things. Fashion designers may well exploit the explanatory value of echoing the past in this way when creating the new, technology-enabled clothes of tomorrow.

The convergence of fashion and technology will also affect the way we choose our clothes each day. When selecting our wardrobe, we will not only have to decide whether we need to wear a jacket or a pullover, and whether their colours match. We will also have to customise those garments in terms of the functionalities that we think we'll need during the day.

New dimensions
The new clothing will empower us in different ways. It will allow us to relax and be entertained, it will allow us to communicate more easily, it will allow us to extend our ability to control our environment and enhance our sense of security, and it will allow us to monitor our health more effectively.

But this is only the beginning. Body monitoring, for instance, does not have to be limited to our own bodies. Watching sports can gain a whole new dimension when, through wireless monitoring devices in clothing, we can observe more of what is 'happening' during performances, monitoring athletes' heart rate, for instance, or measuring the power exerted by a player when taking a golf shot, serving at tennis, starting a rowing race, or taking a penalty

at soccer. This takes us beyond our normal powers of observation: we will be able to see and experience things we have never seen or experienced before.

This highly convenient and direct mode of communication will have unexpected effects in many areas of life. Children, for instance, will be freer to play where they like, since parents will be able to check on their whereabouts from a distance. And as better communication compensates even more effectively for the time delay that inevitably accompanies physical travel, a variety of new benefits will emerge, ranging from medical diagnosis and treatment at a distance, to the rapid location of people in danger.

Smart clothes will also help us live more physically comfortable lives. For example, they will be able to provide an adjustable microclimate for our body. By incorporating appropriate technology, we can have the same jacket keep us warm in winter and cool in summer; or keep our temperature constant as we walk out of an over-air-conditioned building into the tropical heat outside – and back again.

ultimate – modifying the body
The field of wearable electronics is full of opportunities. The simple reason for this is that there still are many ways people can be empowered to achieve their ultimate goal of approaching the gods.

Clothes and other indispensable objects around us are the almost ideal carriers of empowering functions.

I say 'almost' because the ultimate step will be when we have such functionalities incorporated directly into our bodies. ID chips are already being inserted into animals' bodies, and we humans are gradually getting used to the idea of having foreign organs, pacemakers and plastic hips implanted in us for medical purposes. It is only a matter of time before people will be prepared to have chips implanted in their bodies for non-medical purposes.

For thousands of years, people have altered their physical appearance to make themselves more attractive, and in many cultures around the world they still do. In Polynesia the body may be tattooed with intricate designs; in New Guinea, rings and rods adorn the nose; in certain parts of Africa, rings and disks are used to extend the neck and lower lip; and in ancient Peru, babies' skulls were bound so that they would take on a specific form as they grew. And in our own culture earrings, body-piercing and tattoos are an increasingly popular way of decorating the body, and cosmetic surgery – from nose-jobs to silicon breast implants and liposuction – is even altering our bodies under the skin.

Attitudes towards the body are changing, and it is quite possible that in a few decades – if not earlier – public opinion will be ready to accept the full consequences of the idea that, to achieve the optimal level of comfort and freedom, many of the tools we now carry around with us will need to be built into the body.

Our physical bodies are, fundamentally, biochemical devices. Extremely sophisticated ones, to be sure, but devices nonetheless. Are we about to move into a stage of evolution in which we become hybrids – a cross between ourselves and digital technology? Will we become the bionic men and women featured in so many TV series and movies? This whole issue goes beyond mere lifestyle transformations and takes this debate into the field of ethics. We may feel like saying 'Heaven forbid!', but we should realise that it is only the logical next step in a development that has been going on since time immemorial.

Shared language
But let us not run ahead of ourselves. For the moment, there are many exciting challenges and opportunities already here. If we are to make the most of them, the fashion, textile and electronics industries will need to find ways of working together and of speaking each other's language, so that we can explore the possibilities that we already have to help people do more, experience more, be more. Because ultimately, that is what we will be doing with technology-enabled clothing: helping people move ever closer towards their goal of self-fulfilment.

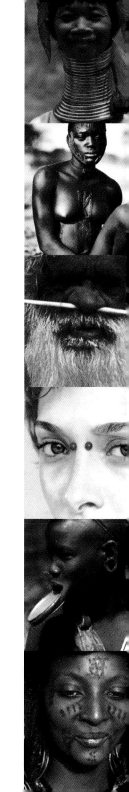

New rules for a new age

Josephine Green

Life is good. Life is bad. Either could be true for the future depending, in part, on what we do with our technology. Technology has and will have increasing power and influence over our everyday life, but this is no guarantee that it will automatically improve the quality of that life. The stunning and sometimes overwhelming possibilities of today's and tomorrow's technology could either enhance or diminish our lives, and so perhaps now, as never before, we need to reflect on the technology decisions we make and their influence on us and society.

How can technology and innovation help us to create a more enriched and, at the same time, more sustainable future? To answer this question we need to understand how we and society are changing and what we will value in the future. Our ongoing research at Philips Design into social and cultural values has highlighted that a new set of beliefs and expectations are emerging deep within so-ciety, as we make the transition from the industrial to the knowledge society. Based on this research, we have identified four 'scripts' or new narratives that can help us think about and innovate for the future: The Mosaic Society, The Explorer Society, The Caring Society and The Sustainable Society. These scripts help us to think first and foremost about people and what they might want, and, from a human perspective, to explore the role and design of technology for the coming era.

The Mosaic Society

If we think of our lives as an empty canvas, then now, as never before, we are called upon to fill in the artwork. We are coming to terms with the fact that the future is more and more what we make of it, and that this is both a freedom and a condemnation. We are freer to take advantage of all the possibilities, but more pressured to 'burn out' in the process. More of us are living alone, moving around the globe, job hopping and practising lifelong learning as we journey along. We no longer follow the set patterns of behaviour, more common to the second half of the 20th century: instead, we choose our own personal goals, ambitions and ways of being. We create our own mosaic of life, made up of a kaleidoscope of simultaneous or sequential relationships, careers and lifestyles. In the faster world of today we want to be empowered but not overpowered, and so we are increasingly looking for anything that can give us control of our lives. We want to be informed, to be entertained, to communicate, irrespective of time, place or circumstances. Perhaps more than anything we want to connect with others and to stay in touch, to feel, in an ever more individualised society, that we belong and have an emotional place to go to. We want all this at our fingertips so that we can juggle our time, options and commitments to our best advantage. As such, we are entering the solution economy that offers personalised and customised products and services that contribute to making each of our lives richer, but at the same time easier and simpler. Technology and innovation that facilitate and enable us to achieve our own mosaic style of living.

The Explorer Society

Through the last century we have been accustomed to having the leisure/pleasure side of our life grow, so that fun, adventure and play have become important elements of our personal expression and gratification. Furthermore, the more 'packaged' and 'processed' world we live in is pushing us to re-affirm and test out our more 'human' feelings and emotions. This includes experiencing the exhilaration from the harder 'thrills' of extreme sports and high-risk experiences to the more 'sensory' enjoyment through the enhancement of all our senses and our moods. In this search we are looking for products that help to monitor or enrich these activities. We also search for products that are not only functional, but also trigger our emotions and speak to our soul. Products that satisfy and please not only our practical needs, but also our 'soft' needs in terms of how they look, feel, sound and even smell. Doing, being and experiencing become more fluid and we look for this total experience not only at exceptional moments, but also in our daily business. Feeding our emotions and our senses not only makes us feel good, it also fosters creativity and a child-like sense of wonder and discovery. Perhaps we are fine-tuning our bodies, our minds, our emotions and our senses because we anticipate that in the future we shall need all of these to grasp the opportunities presented to us and to navigate the complexity of a post-modern world. In the experience economy we want functionality, but also aesthetics, taste and style, and so we look for technology and innovation to go beyond the functional to the emotional and the psychological.

The Caring Society

The old 'security blankets' of the industrial era, such as the welfare state, are disappearing. We are more on our own, our populations are ageing and the gap is widening between the rich and the poor. Furthermore, our new world seems increasingly to encourage performance and productivity, over caring, love and friendship. It is not surprising, therefore, that we are concerned about our mental and physical well-being, our safety and our security. We search for things and relationships that can help take care of us, that can nurture us, that can keep us safe while at home or on the move, that can protect us from harm, physical or environmental. In this context, innovation and technology can only make sense if they contribute to our peace of mind, helping us to feel secure, safe and protected, but not surveyed and controlled. The nightmare scenario of 'big brother' is when relationships break down and technology takes over, so people, not technology, need to be at the heart of a care economy. Technology can revitalise local communities and relationships by facilitating the exchange of knowledge and by stimulating shared experiences.

The Sustainable Society

More of us are becoming aware that environmental damage is directly affecting our health and well-being, and that this damage is not caused by some 'exceptional' disasters but by the negative daily impact of the way we produce and consume. We are becoming aware that we have to change our ways as we go forward and consume not less, but better. There are signs that we can continue to receive the benefits we expect and not damage the environment. In all our future 'scripts' a common thread emerges: that the world is in fact dematerialising. The Solution, Experience and Care Economies can deliver benefits through less material services and solutions. Enjoying downloaded music is less material than buying CDs; consuming an experience is more bits than atoms; working and studying at home for part of the time is less polluting than travelling. Information and communication technology can contribute to the environment by delivering benefits and services that do not heavily tax or pollute the earth's resources. In the final analysis we have to think about how innovation and technology can further a Sustainable Economy.

For the New Nomads we have started to design some solutions around the needs emerging from our futures research. To create a seamless integration between people, textiles and electronics that will enable us to reach out to the world, to stretch our capabilities and possibilities, while at the same time conserving our own and, as our research continues, the planet's energy.

We began by asking how innovation and technology could enhance our future quality of life. In the last analysis, however, it is not technology, but the value system in which it operates that will determine how far it will enhance rather than diminish our future quality of life. If we accept that the future is always more in our hands, then we have to put in place values and processes that can nurture and care for that future. We need to create 'new rules' for a new age.

Wearable electronics

Clive van Heerden

Jack Mama

David Eves

Building upon Philips Design's initial exploration of wearable electronics as part of its Vision of the Future project, in the late 1990s Philips instigated a fresh approach to future lifestyle and fashion by creating a multi-disciplinary team to look at the integration of electronics into clothing.

The idea of clothing containing electronics is, in itself, not new. The Media Lab at Massachusetts Institute of Technology (MIT), for instance, has for some years now been studying the possibilities of 'wearable computing'. Having a strong consumer electronics focus, Philips chose to go down a different route, exploring consumer applications.

Climate for change

In 1997/98 there were a number of trends in consumer electronics, fashion design and consumer behaviour that were significant in forming the backdrop to the Wearable Electronics project.

Miniaturisation

Our research indicated that consumers wanted to be connected and equipped with tools for every possible eventuality, without the inconvenience of having to carry around multiple devices. Accordingly, they associated miniaturisation with sophistication and progress, and were demanding smaller products with an increasing array of functionality. The rapid technological advances taking place at the time meant that the electronics industry was more than capable of providing such miniaturised devices.

However, consumers were being forced to carry around products that were defined by other people's interpretation of their needs in specific situations. Companies making phones, personal digital assistants (PDAs) and personal audio players were interpreting needs and anticipating use in a way that rarely matched actual practice. The cellular phone, the pager, the PDA and the personal audio device all contained components that duplicated each other, yet were non-transferable. Even after years of cellular telephony and portable computing, people were being hindered by a lack of connectivity as these devices were unable to share components and communicate with one another remotely. The solutions were inelegant and inefficient and, far from enabling and enhancing consumers' lifestyles, were in fact becoming a hindrance.

Complexity

The functionality embedded in the various electronic devices was often complicated and inaccessible. Why, for example, was it necessary for each individual device to have its own address book or phone list? Why were message editors not interchangeable? Even when the devices were supposed to speak to each other, they seldom did so without complex connections and considerable know-how on the part of the user.

Control interfaces were dense, complex and codified, and while these products promised to simplify our lives, they invariably did not serve their intended purpose. And as they became smaller and smaller, they became too intricate for users to navigate competently. Also, by employing virtual, screen-based interfaces, users were forced to translate their intuitive knowledge of real processes into a layered maze of decisions with no consistent meaning.

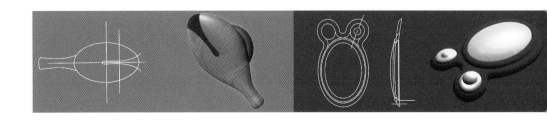

Wearable solutions

The combination of industry supply and consumer demand thus generated an inherent conflict: electronic devices that were smaller and incorporated more complex functionalities were becoming increasingly unusable. We could start to alleviate this problem by redesigning clusters of functionalities controlled by human gesture, speech and location. Clothing would become the product medium, with an increased 'interface real estate' – the entire surface area of the body would be available to create controls that were easier to use.

Pioneering approach

On the basis of the trends observed and with a clear vision of how wearable electronics might be able to address the conflict of miniaturisation and complexity versus ease of use, a radical new approach to design research was initiated by Philips. Despite the associated risk of entering uncharted territory, it was vital to develop a new vocabulary and language for both the working process and the project content. Philips was entering a potential new product domain ahead of its competitors and therefore faced a host of problems and issues never encountered before. A flexible approach to working was to prove the key to success.

Multi-disciplinary research

At the end of the 20th century, the type of research needed to produce innovative new products called for a range of capabilities and skills that were not traditionally found in research laboratories, which at the start of the 1990s had been very much the domain of the computer scientist and the electronic engineer. Now, Philips started experimenting with the creation of multi-disciplinary groups that brought designers and engineers to the research program. A series of academic collaborations with design and technology colleges ensured a constant flow of students drawn from a wide range of so-called 'non-technical' disciplines, including animators, character designers, writers, vehicle designers, industrial design engineers and business students.

During the summer of 1997, a team, initially comprising a fashion designer, an industrial design engineer and an electronic engineer, was formed at the laboratories in Redhill (UK). They were given a fairly wide brief: to explore the field of electronic fashion. Forcing together such a mix of disciplines generated a creative tension, a tension founded upon a deep-rooted cultural antagonism between engineering and design problem-solving methodologies. Managing

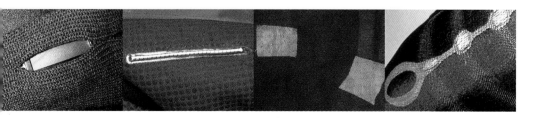

this tension in such a way as to harness the creativity inherent in such a multi-disciplinary collaboration (which grew to encompass textile designers, software engineers, consumer trend analysts and socio-cultural researchers) engendered a new way of working.

The project got under way with the production of concept garments. In parallel with the conceptual work, design research was initiated to understand and generate the enabling technologies that would bring the vision of smart apparel to life. Key elements in this respect were the MIT-pioneered Personal Area Network (or Body Area Network as it is often referred to now), smart textiles, and wear and care issues.

Body Area Network

The Body Area Network provides the backbone for smart apparel. It allows the transport of data, power and control signals within the user's 'personal space'. Modular devices with functions shared by different applications can be hooked up to it: for example, a single display can be used for phone call information and personal audio track selection. Intelligent software ensures that the devices cooperate in a natural way: muting the CD player when the phone rings,

for instance. This modular network architecture and a user-centric design make it possible to configure the system to match the user's preferred interaction style, rather than requiring the user to adapt his or her behaviour to the system, or worse still, to a whole set of very different products.

Smart textiles

The challenge was to make conductive textiles that are also soft and warm to touch. These garment raw materials enable us to move audio, data and power around a garment relatively easily.

Conductive fibres can be integrated into knitwear and woven materials, and conductive inks allow electrically active patterns to be printed directly onto fabrics.

The team at Redhill tested thousands of yarns to find those with the most favourable properties and then went on to develop its own fabrics that exhibited excellent behaviour as conductors, insulators and sensors, e.g. a material with a conductivity that changes in a predictable way as it is stretched! Putting these materials together as a garment also required specialist skills.

Wear and care - silicon and silk

The integration of electronics into the fabric and structure of clothing and other products promises to overcome the intrinsic contradiction of shrinking size and elusive usability – while the electronics are smaller, the user interface is nevertheless much larger and potentially more intuitive. The real estate of the body provides endless opportunities to distribute controls, displays, audio feedback, power sources, etc. Natural movements, gestures and speech can all be utilised to control and direct the application.

However, the hard, inflexible nature of electronic components and the soft, tactile nature of clothing fabrics do not mix naturally. The life cycle of clothes is totally unsuited to the incorporation of electronics. We often think of our mobile devices as being quite robust, still capable of working when used in the rain. However, normal weather conditions are benign compared with the hostile environment encountered inside a washing machine. Washing machines, tumble dryers, steam irons and solvents used in dry cleaning conflict with the electronic needs of insulation, inflexible connectors and power sources. The materials used in electronics, such as copper, are also subject to the problem of oxidation and add friction to parts of a garment.

Even though in the early stages of wearable electronics we designed electronic components to be unplugged, a substantial part of the wiring, peripherals and connectors will be totally integrated and therefore must be able to withstand washing or other forms of garment care.

Questioning minds

In addressing issues such as these, the multi-disciplinary approach adopted allowed the participating disciplines to question one another – to question assumptions, methodology and professional techniques. Contradictions had to be resolved: for instance, the designers were demanding more flexible and robust properties, while the technologists were insisting on components being located in areas of the garment that both distorted the aesthetics and compromised the comfort of the clothing. In the pursuit of a wholly effective compromise, each discipline was urged to discover new, innovative ways of working and to build upon shared know-how. In this way, a number of disciplines underwent a process of redefinition and restructuring. Mirroring these dynamics, the content of the project itself involved a similar metaphor of deconstruction and redefinition . . .

Deconstruct to redefine

We initially looked at five product groupings – cellular phones, mobile computers, pagers, personal audio and semiconductors. With the exception of semiconductors, all of these products are sold on the basis of the amazing things they can do in their miniature form. However, it was this fundamental contradiction between size and complexity that was making them unworkable. Any user carrying around these four products had four displays, four sets of batteries, four keypads, multiple databases, speakers, ringers, etc. Our objective was to try to understand the overlaps in what they did and how they might share resources.

Cyborg?

Most of the research in the public domain at the time seemed to focus on mobile computing, with either military or industrial applications. The objective of much of this work was to augment humans to become super-human – the ability to know everything with on-board databases, to record everything, or, in the case of muscle fibres, even to enhance the human physically to become super-human.

Little effort seemed to be being made to examine the issue 'from the other side'. How could person-borne technology help us in ways that did not require humans to adapt to machines? Imagine a network that enabled you to plug individual functionalities onto your body! Imagine an address book in the form of a button that is both the symbolic representation of the addresses that are important to its user and also the actual memory of these addresses. And imagine if any other devices needing to access these addresses could do so simply by establishing contact with the object, and that all of these objects (displays, batteries, speakers, keypads, etc.) were intelligent enough to know what other objects were connected to the network and modified their behaviour accordingly.

We were convinced that the locomotives that would drag these products into existence would be the compelling applications that matched actual, rather than imposed, human needs. Technology that disappeared into the fabric rather than weighing us down.

Ritual of dress

We looked at the ritual of dress – how people assembled their personal identities through clothes that combined the functionalities of protection, thermal insulation, waterproofing, etc. with the personal and cultural qualities of aesthetics and identity. We explored how this metaphor might extend to the way people might assemble

their electronic functionalities to create truly personal portable electronic devices.

Sub-cultural antennae: early adopters

We sought to identify those groups whose lifestyle most suited 'intelligent clothing'. Clearly, if we looked at the range of fashion options, we could target applications at all sections of the market, but in the late 1990s most groups would still have found the concept of electronics integrated into their clothing too futuristic. While we could identify a trend towards integration due to incessant miniaturisation and modularisation, for most people the idea of washing their electronics or hanging them up to re-charge was still too extreme.

Accordingly, we looked at the sub-cultures where we felt early adoption of wearable solutions would occur – clubbers; active sportspeople who wear high-performance sportswear for extreme sports, e.g. rock climbers, cyclists, snowboarders, runners, etc.; and urban commuters, e.g. financial district workers who work on the move and 'live in the fast lane'. By studying these groups we were able to identify how people were using existing products and where

the limitations of technology were causing frustration. These groups needed technology and were looking for ways to integrate products into the ensemble of clothing and equipment characteristic of their own specific culture.

Clubbers, for instance, wanted to feel 'connected', to know what was going on somewhere else at any given moment, but they did not want to carry around pagers or phones. Increasingly, the top London clubs, for instance, issue pagers, and an enormously high number of clubbers carry mobile phones, so people are carrying around multiple devices with nowhere to put them. We developed the concept of 'pageable knickers' to overcome the problem of where to carry a pager, while at the same time making a fashion statement. Likewise, the use of electro-luminescent panels in clothing had already started to infiltrate club fashion, and materials such as light-emitting thread and LED arrays were becoming quite common.

We developed clothing that gave people the ability to sample sounds and feed back to the club experience – clothing that was interactive – by creating variable resistance in the knit. As a dancer

moves, so the biometric feedback affects the music. Similarly, we developed an outfit that enabled a club DJ to perform while moving around the club, i.e. not tied to the conventional DJ station.

Breaking down, dressing up

It will take time for an installed base of 'electronic clothes' to emerge, and this will occur in parallel with the deconstruction of electronic objects as we know them today. At present, consumers typically have one mobile phone, which has a form reminiscent of the traditional terrestrial phone. As phones and other devices become modular, we will move from a situation where we own one phone to a situation where we have many phones integrated into garments. By modularising the product, we can separate the 'brain' from the other components. The 'phone' module will be no more than a button that simply plugs into the clothes that are already equipped with an infrastructure to support it.

Like the carriage clock of 300 years ago that subsequently became a pocket watch and then a wristwatch, personal electronic devices will become items that can be worn as jewellery or accessories. The shift to totally integrated electronics will follow a period where products have dual functions: they are both the material embodiment of a specific set of functionalities and are adaptable for wearing on the body. Also, for the successful introduction of Body Area Networks incorporated in items of clothing, certain standards will have to emerge.

Inhibitors

As with many new technological products, like the answer-phone, which often intimidated callers into *not* leaving messages, or personal audio, which became a source of tension on public transport by generating ambient noise, the introduction of cellular telephony has created a new set of behaviour patterns: taboos exist about where they should be seen and not heard, or where and how loud they ring, and so on. Naturally, such mores differ from one culture to the next.

Certain cultural and behavioural inhibitors are sure to emerge in the case of smart apparel. People wonder whether they will have to buy multiple phones to match different jackets. And what if the garment is not 'wearable-ready' and will not accept electronic objects?

The end of the beginning

User tests in many major cities around the world have indicated that the fashion/technology fusion of wearable electronics could be a winning combination. In the future, clothes will be an important part of the user's personal network. This technology will be a companion for long periods of time, natural in its interaction and proactive in its support. The interface will evolve from a personal to an intimate one. The garments shown in the following section offer a visionary glimpse of what might become possible over the coming years and relate to five distinct areas:

perform - digital suits for professional business people
work out - electronic sportswear
enjoy - interactive playsuits for kids
connect - wired streetwear for youth
embody - enhanced body care and adornment

As researchers and designers of electronic equipment, our desire is to provide people with tools that will help them communicate, stimulate their brains and senses with entertainment and information, and enable them to do more and achieve greater freedom of action in a wide variety of fields. This amplification and exteriorisation of people's powers and capabilities through technology has to be effected with maximum ease.

In line with this, we believe it is vital that 'smart clothing' is geared towards serving real human needs and desires, offering the wearer comfort, convenience and tailor-made functionality for the purpose of information, communication and entertainment.

Our ultimate vision is that people will consider wearable electronics as part of getting dressed, that in future all clothes will contain some infrastructure and some elements that add value to the network of electronics that we have around our bodies. Against this background, we will continue to push the limits in distributed electronics, control functionality, garment construction and fabric technology.

perform

digital suits for professionals

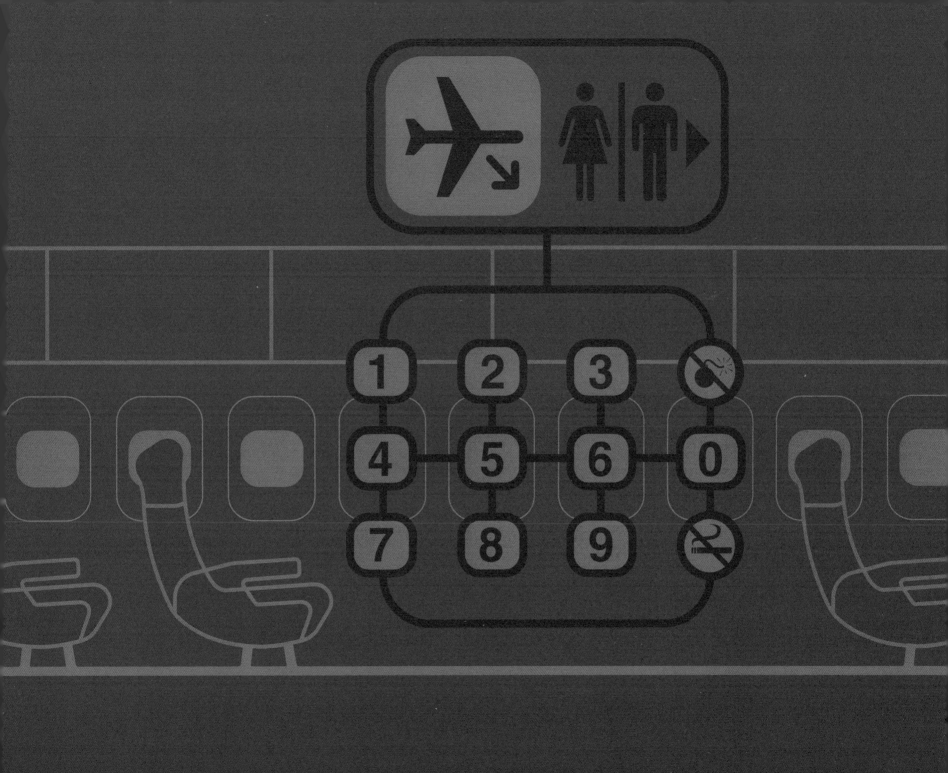

nomadic working

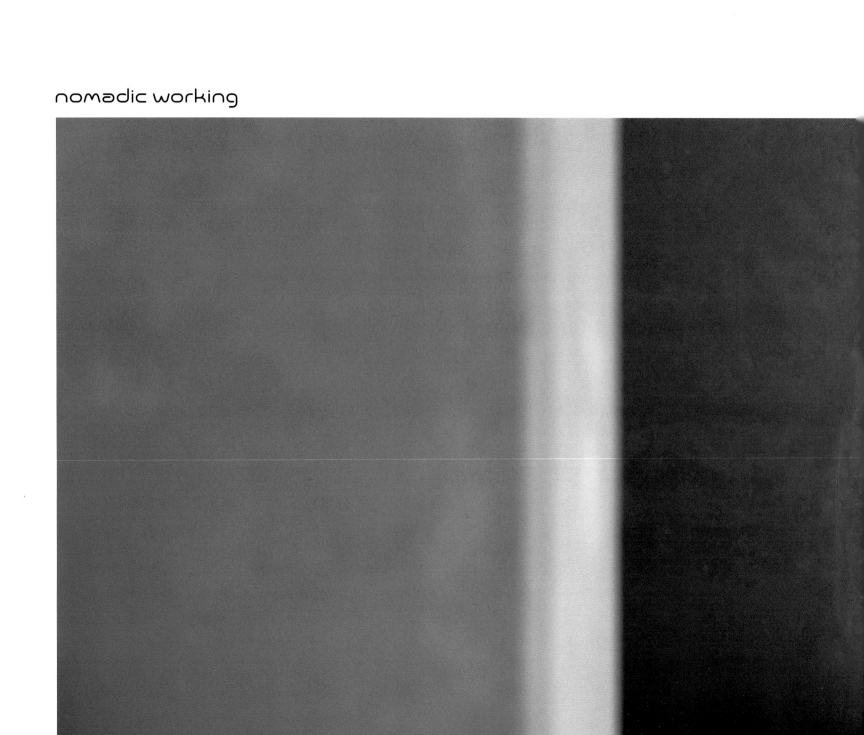

nomadic working

Imagine what it would be like to be truly travelling light, or even empty-handed, while retaining full and direct access to information and maximising the on-the-move communication capability that can be so decisive in today's e-business environment!

In the morning, when dressing, the user selects the devices needed based on the schedule for the day ahead and plugs them into the clothing he or she has chosen to wear. The electronic

devices are divided up into several small single-function modules. The small earpiece is comfortable and can be worn all day, and a speech device is integrated into a detachable 'button' on the inside of the jacket. The display is flexible and integrated into the fabric. A fabric 'keypad' drops down from a jacket cuff, providing overall physical control. The devices are treated as 'hidden secrets' embedded in the garment and invisible to others until such time as the wearer decides to use one of them.

nomadic working

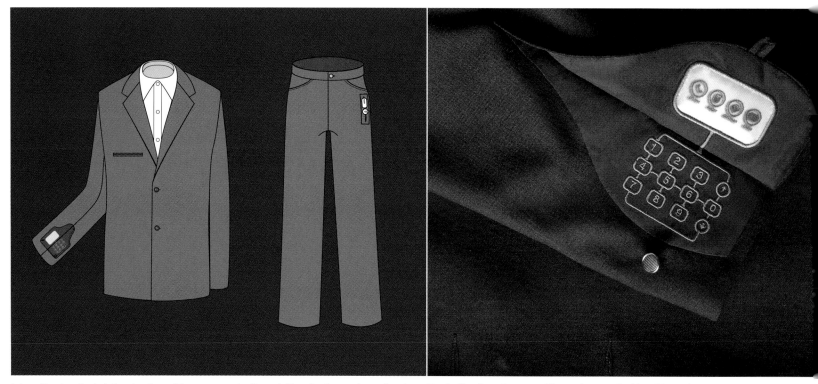

Integration in a finely tailored suit provides a communication solution allowing maximum freedom   Conductive threads are used to create an embroidered keypad

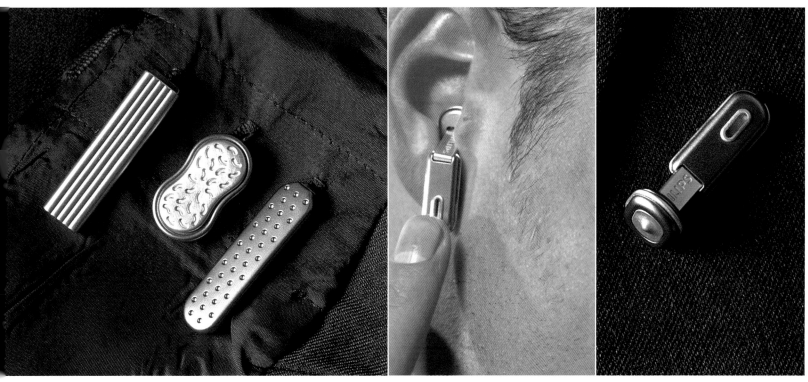

All communication tools are removable, pocketable fashion accessories   The phone earpiece, also an item of jewellery, can be stored in a button hole when not in use

imaginair

imaginair

The shift from 'portable' to 'wearable' will inevitably affect work-wear. Air hostesses, hospital staff, repair workers, etc., all perform jobs in which they require electronic aids that can easily be located on the body for reasons of safety and efficiency.

This air hostess's uniform incorporates a personal digital assistant with flexible LCD screen, a wireless earpiece and a microphone. She can use these to communicate with the other members of the cabin crew and the pilots while she is serving the passengers. All seating arrangements, traveller profiles, meal requests, flight information and so on can be carried on the sleeve. The system uses infrared connections while airborne and incorporates shielding fabrics to protect the wearer and to allow the on-board electronic equipment to be used safely.

imaginair

The Imaginair suit is designed for comfort and efficiency

The suit is both practical and elegant, giving the air hostess added confidence

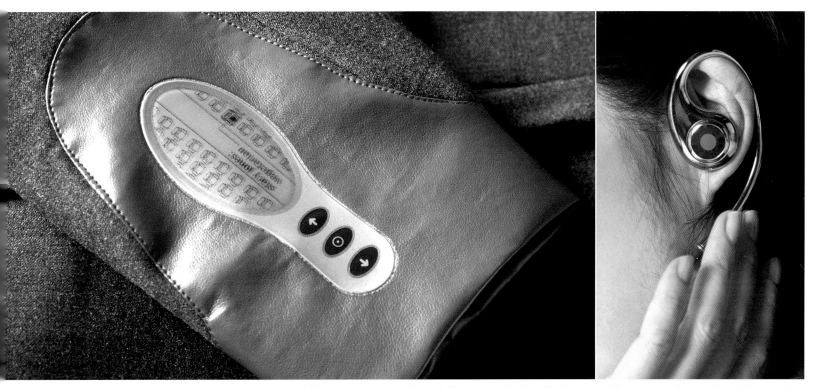

The personal digital assistant on the sleeve provides passenger information and allows communication with the crew

Ergonomic wireless earpiece with microphone

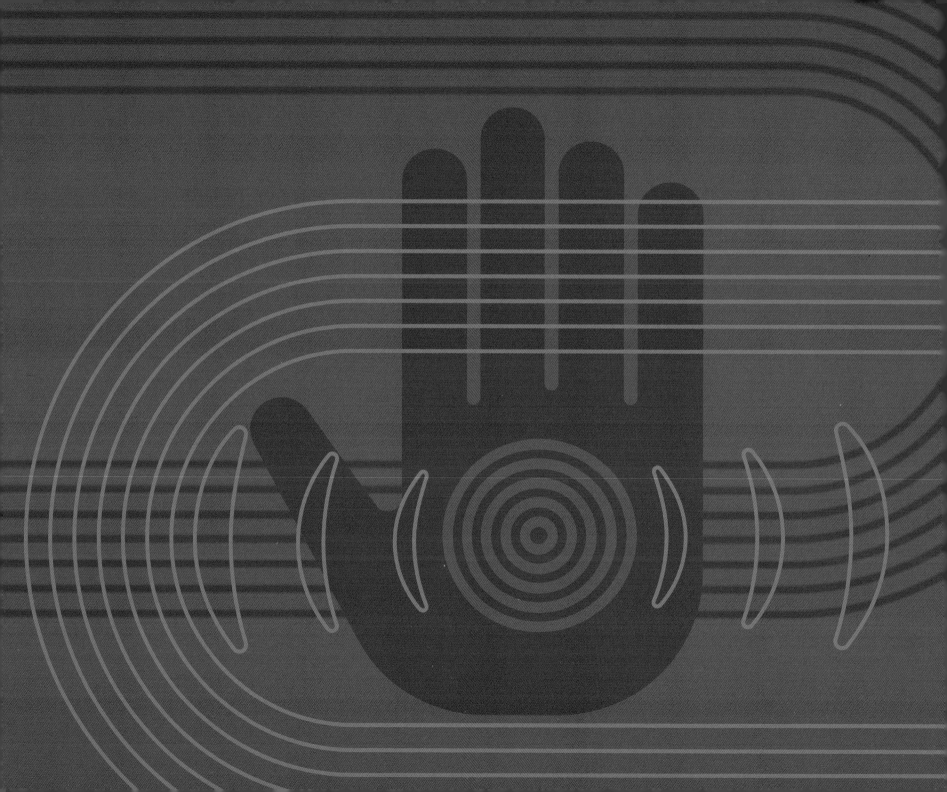

workout

electronic sportswear

keep on moving

keep on moving

One group that is eminently suited to electronic apparel is the exercise community. Of the millions of people who exercise on a regular basis, a huge proportion work out with personal audio in the form of a CD, cassette or digital music player. None of these devices are entirely suitable for exercise, because they are relatively bulky, uncomfortable and tend to skip tracks if subjected to any impact. Joggers have often complained about having to have wires hanging from their headphones; they would also like to eliminate the bulk and discomfort associated with holding a heavy plastic device or carrying it on their belt.

With Internet delivery of music, we saw the possibility of creating integrated audio functionality with no moving parts that is also designed to track the performance of the user. Using the processing power of a digital audio player, we could add functions that would improve the performance of the athlete. The Virtual Coach, for instance, monitors and regulates the pace of training. A training log and performance analysis derived from a series of biometric sensors is then fed back to other devices in the home. This intimate understanding of physical performance and detailed management of the training schedule greatly enhances the way people experience a sometimes tedious activity.

The jogging pants are ideal for dynamic activity. The breathable fabric allows the freedom of natural movement while running, walking or jogging. Inside the pocket there is a knitted circuit which links to the conductive printed interface. This controls the solid-state portable audio device through the connecting network. The interface is positioned for easy use while the wearer is active.

keep on moving

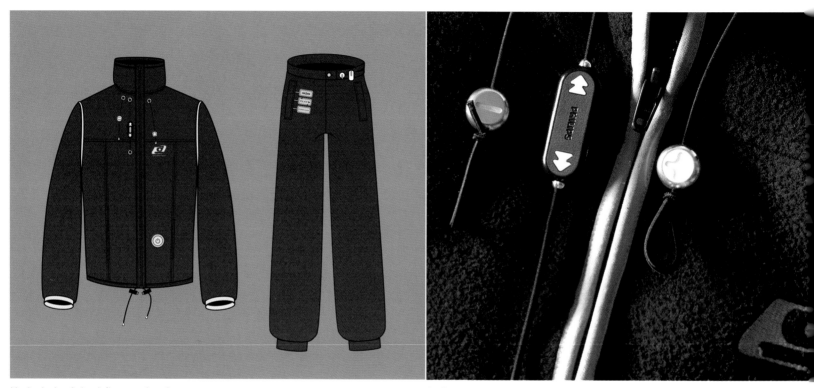

Men's electronic track fleece and pants

Audio controls are activated by pulling the cords

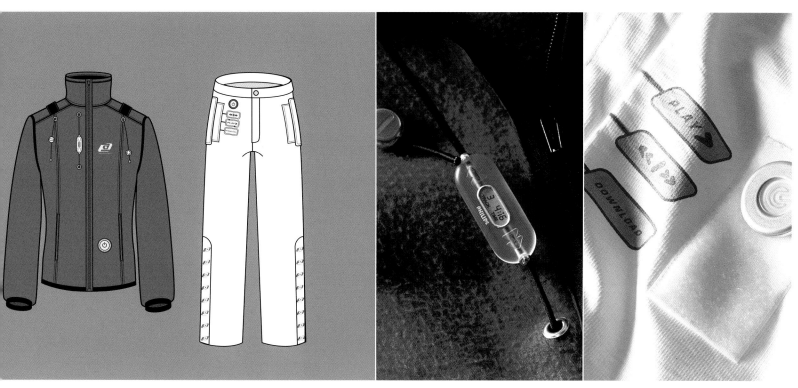

Women's electronic sportswear   Cord-switch with integrated display   Audio player operated via printed interface

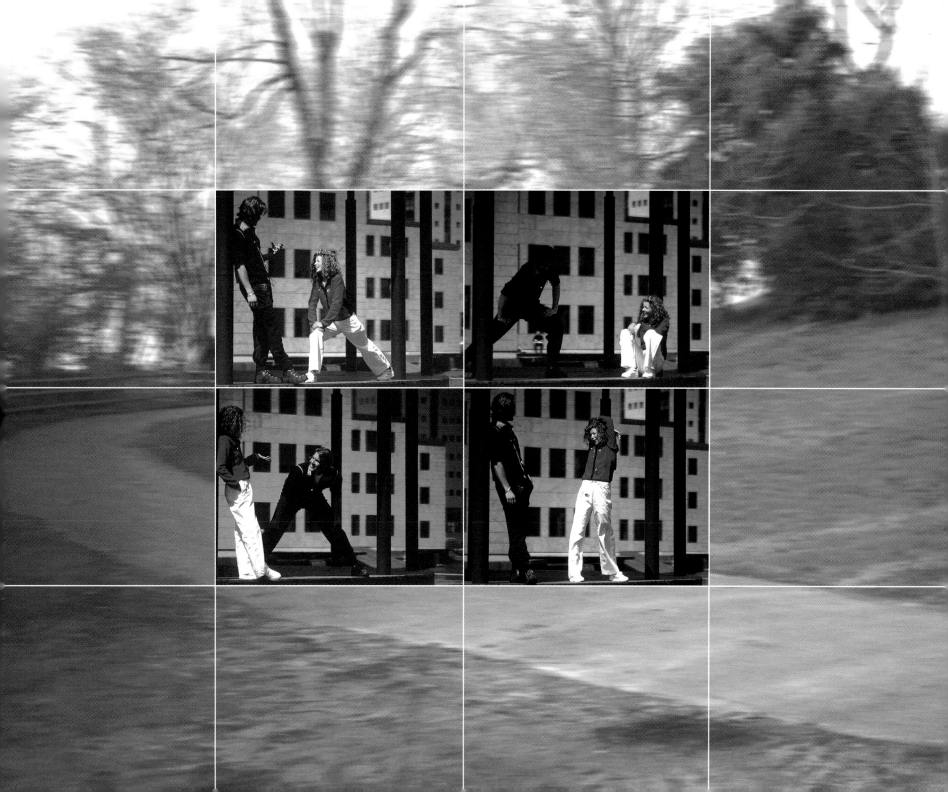

perfect performance

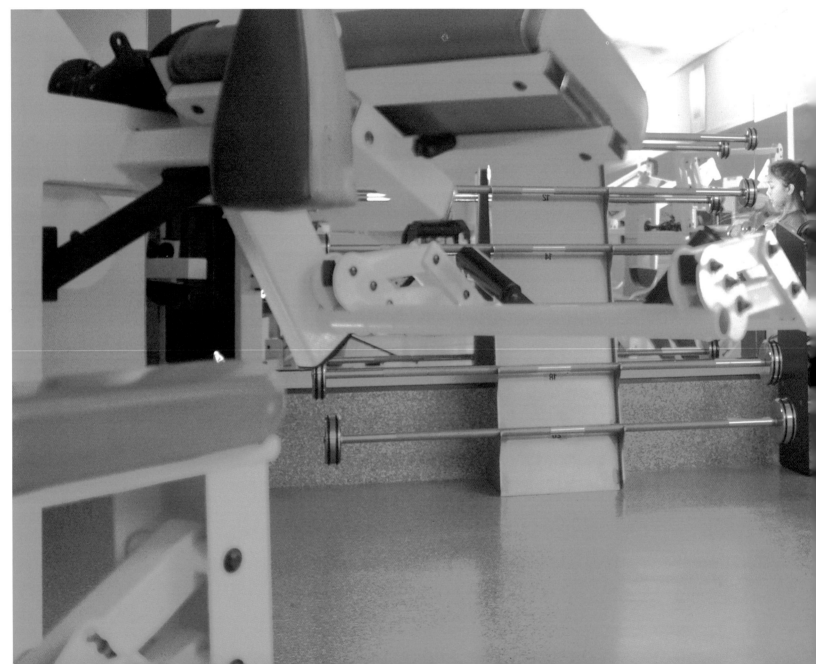

perfect performance

High-performance sportswear can incorporate embedded technologies that offer a combination of audio features and ways to
monitor the body. Like the jogging outfits, these fitness outfits
have biometric sensors integrated into the fabric. The integration
of biometric sensors into clothing to monitor pulse, blood pres-
sure, body temperature, respiration and other vital indicators,
which are then displayed to allow the wearer to manage his/her
fitness program and communicated wirelessly to other devices,
has enormous appeal in the field of high-performance sports.

In these outfits, conductive embroidery and printing are used to
operate a solid-state audio device that has been integrated into
the garment. The stretch fabrics from which the suits are made
provide feedback, allowing the wearer to correct posture and
movement and so achieve the optimum workout.

perfect performance

This sports outfit combines audio functionality and body monitoring

Bio-sensor bra

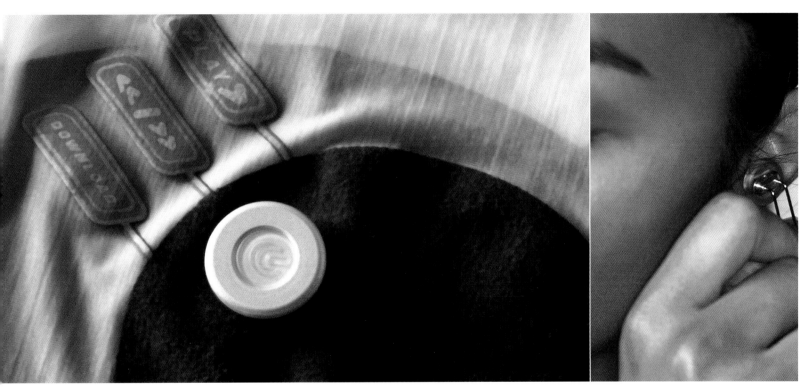

Audio device with conductive printed interface

Lightweight wireless earpiece

staying alive

staying alive

This coat has been made for those who are not satisfied with merely spectating, but who actively seek out challenges and adventures, 'taking it to the limit'. Designed for use in the toughest conditions, the coat has integrated GPS (Global Positioning System) functionality. The interface on the cuff provides the wearer with data relating to position, distance, body and atmospheric temperature, etc. Thanks to the barometric and altitude sensors incorporated into the suit, the mountaineer knows what types of weather front to expect. With these embedded safety features the user is equipped to cope with harsh, mountainous terrain.

staying alive

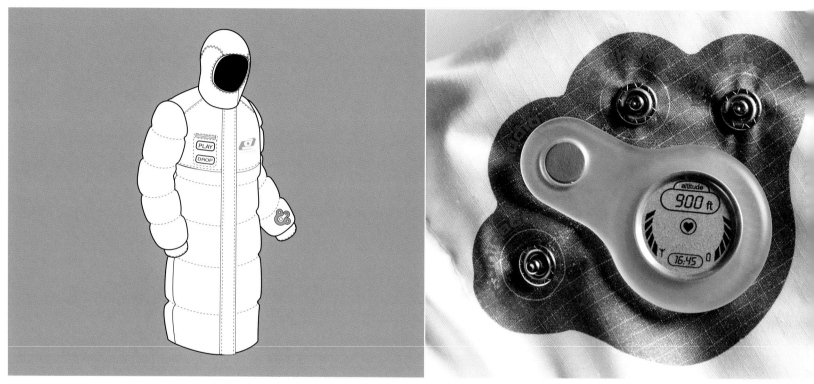

This mountaineer's suit is made for extreme conditions

The cuff interface provides readings for altitude, longitude, distance and temperature

The embroidered *electronique* logo is found on all sports garments

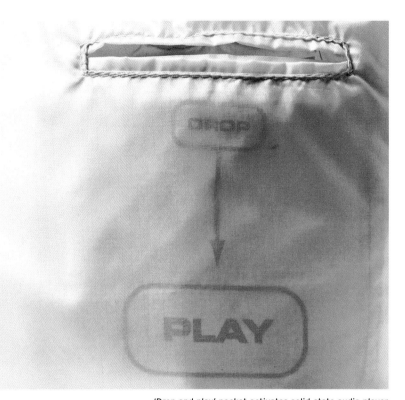

'Drop and play' pocket activates solid-state audio player

techno surfer

techno surfer

Participation in extreme sports is on the increase due to the growing need, often not fulfilled by other aspects of modern living, to feel truly alive. High-risk extreme sports can benefit from innovative technology embedded in garments. Creating a virtual network, such technology is not only beneficial to the wearer, but also to the service and rescue teams that are often called into action on behalf of people involved in these sports.

This outfit contains electronics that provide both fun and safety on the slopes. Equipped with electronic ski passes, radio links, satellite positioning, warning displays, temperature sensors and heating materials, this outfit will enable the dedicated snowboarder to cope with any conditions. Many potentially life-saving features have been built in. If the integrated thermometer detects that the body temperature has fallen below a certain level, the fabric of the garment will heat up instantly. The positioning system can locate the snowboarder, and an orientation sensor knows straight away if he or she has suffered a fall. A proximity sensor on the back of the jacket detects if another skier or snowboarder is getting too close, and a warning hand icon lights up to tell them to back off.

And all of this to the sound of our own music: motion detectors monitor the rhythm of the wearer's movements, feeding back and constantly re-shaping the music track being mixed by the snowboarder's body movements.

techno surfer

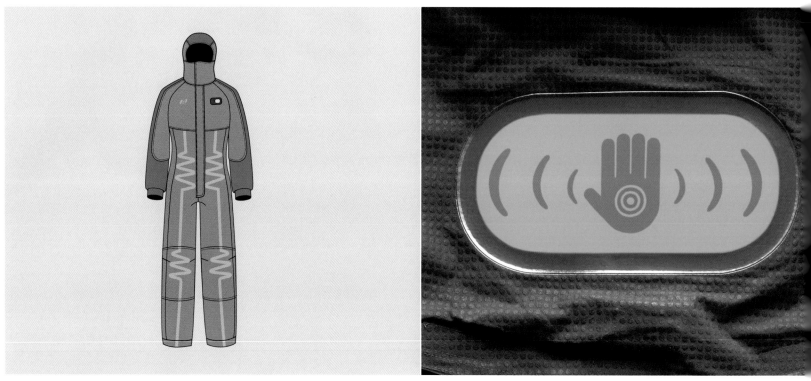

Safety is a must when living life on the edge

The display flashes a warning signal when other skiers or snowboarders are getting too clo

Hood made of breathable fabrics   Ski pass with GPS functionality   Printed touch sensors on the glove activate the functionalities on the head display

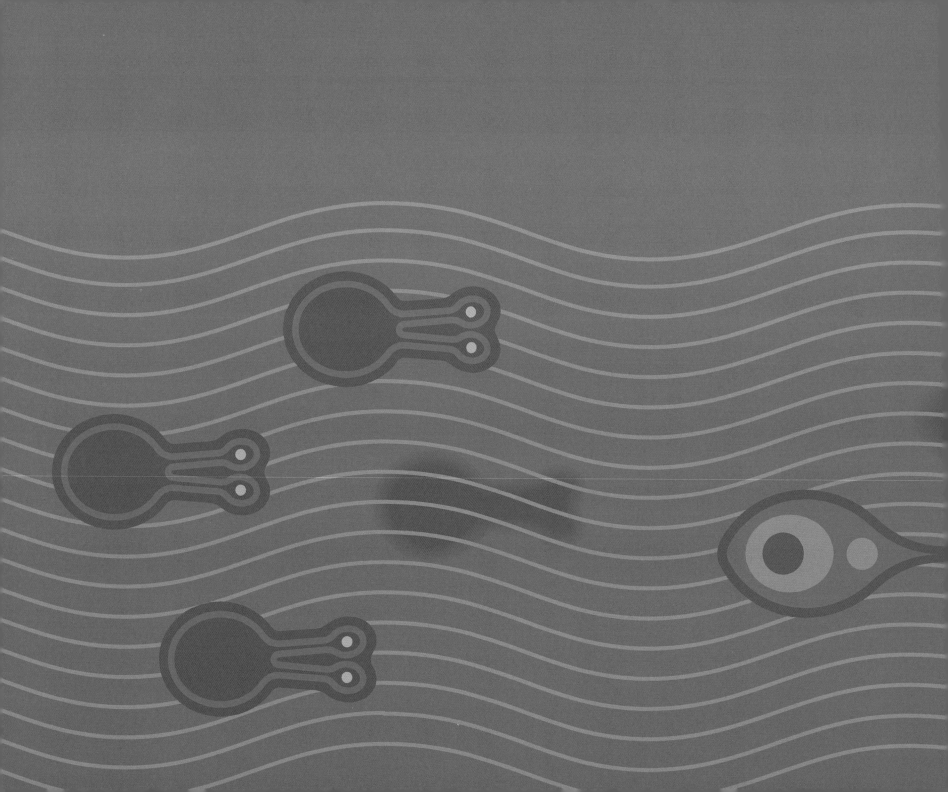

interactive playsuits for kids

enjoy

no kidding!

no kidding!

Designed to give parents peace of mind, this garment uses mobile phone and camera technology to pinpoint their kids' position. To the children, however, the coat is first and foremost a device that they can use to play exciting outdoor games. In other words, it allows mum and dad to keep track of the kids, without them being aware that their whereabouts are being monitored. This is achieved using fabric antennas, radio tagging and miniature remote cameras.

In addition to this monitoring capability, we have devised a series of games in which physical characters with identity chips can be attached to the respective garments. The child sees the character that represents another child as a monster or animal on his or her screen. As the children move around, their 'characters' can be seen moving on the screen. The children play together and have to think up scenarios to explain what is happening on their screens.

no kidding!

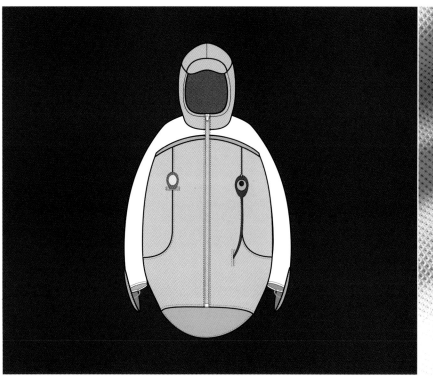

This garment lets children have fun while ensuring their security

This small remote camera can be detached to allow close-up shots

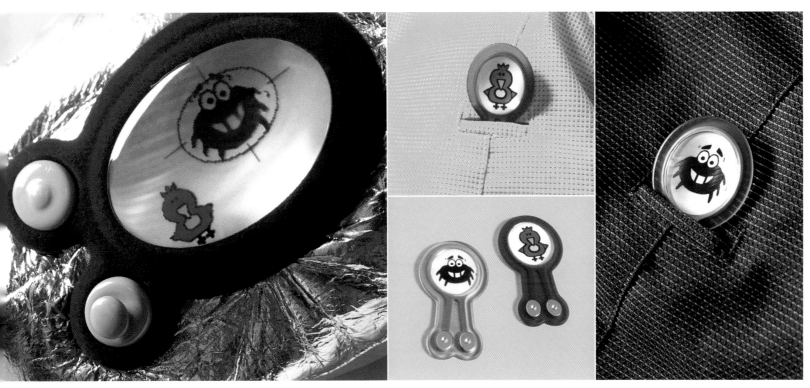

The display on the sleeve reveals the presence of another child as an animated character

Once slipped into the pocket, the tag reveals the child's character and the game starts

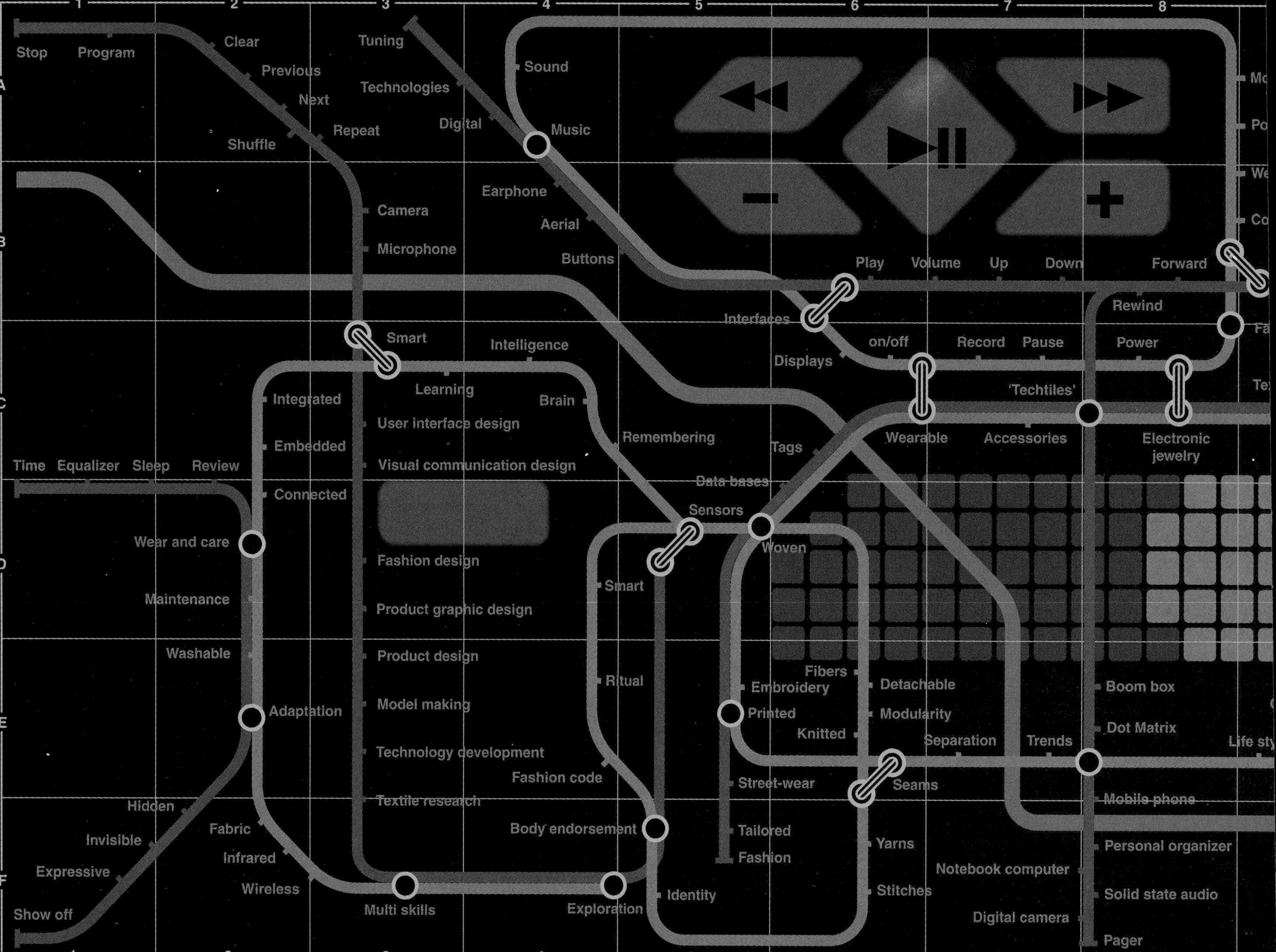

1 2 3 4 5 6 7 8

A B C D E

Stop Program Clear Tuning Sound
Previous Technologies
Next Digital Music
Repeat
Shuffle Earphone
Camera Aerial
Microphone Buttons

▶❙❙

Play Volume Up Down Forward
Interfaces Rewind
Smart Intelligence on/off Record Pause Power
Displays 'Techtiles'
Integrated Learning Brain
Embedded User interface design Remembering Tags Wearable Accessories Electronic jewelry
Visual communication design
Time Equalizer Sleep Review Data bases
Connected Sensors Woven
Fashion design
Wear and care Smart
Product graphic design
Maintenance Ritual Fibers Detachable Boom box
Product design Embroidery Modularity
Washable Printed Dot Matrix
Model making Knitted Separation Trends
Adaptation Technology development
Fashion code Street-wear Seams Mobile phone
Hidden Textile research Tailored Yarns Personal organizer
Fabric Body endorsement Fashion
Invisible Infrared Notebook computer
Expressive Wireless Stitches Solid state audio
Show off Multi skills Exploration Identity Digital camera Pager

Mo Po We Co Fa Te Life sty

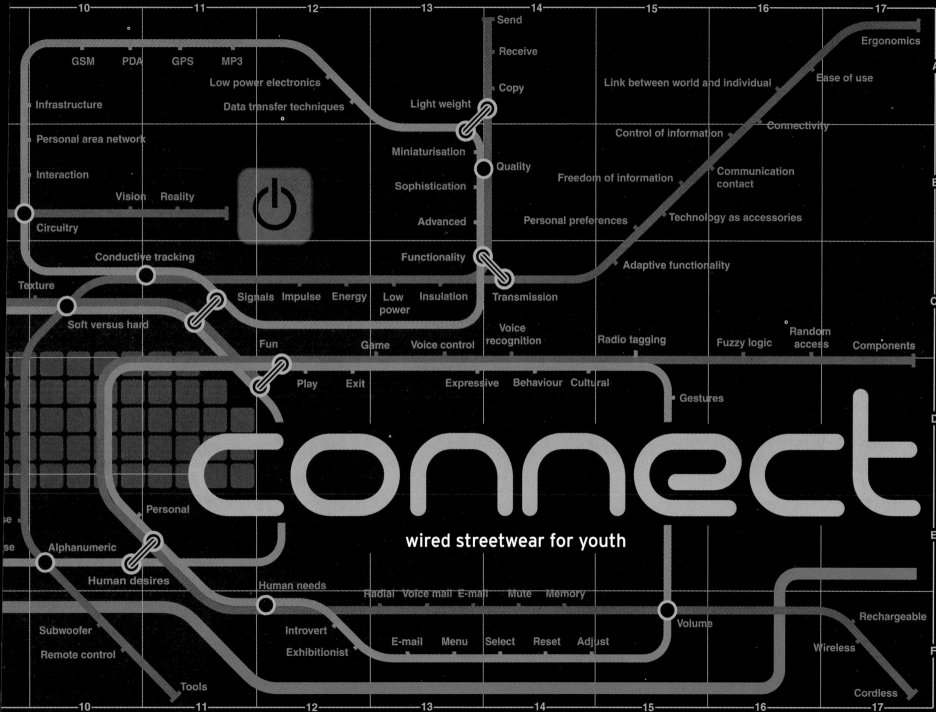

queen of clubs

The contradiction between needing to be connected and not wanting to carry electronic products is very evident in the club scene. The electronics embedded in this garment not only provide phone and pager functions, but also enable clubbers to interact with their surroundings through body movements which are sensed by the garment.

Designed for clubland, the top of the outfit interacts with the music so that, as the fabric stretches and relaxes, it causes the audio and light settings in the club to change. The bottom part of the outfit – pageable knickers with lights that flash when someone is trying to get in touch – allows contact to be made with other 'interesting' persons inside or outside the club.

queen of clubs

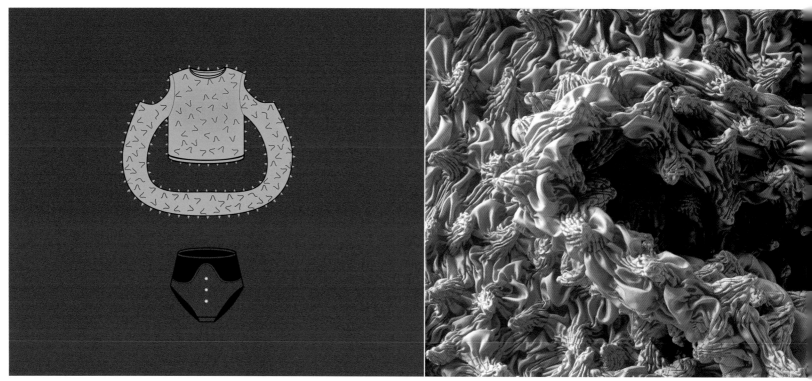

Interactive clubbing outfit

Stretchable fabrics interact with the wearer's surroundings, providing a new sensory exper

Pageable knickers flash when a message is received

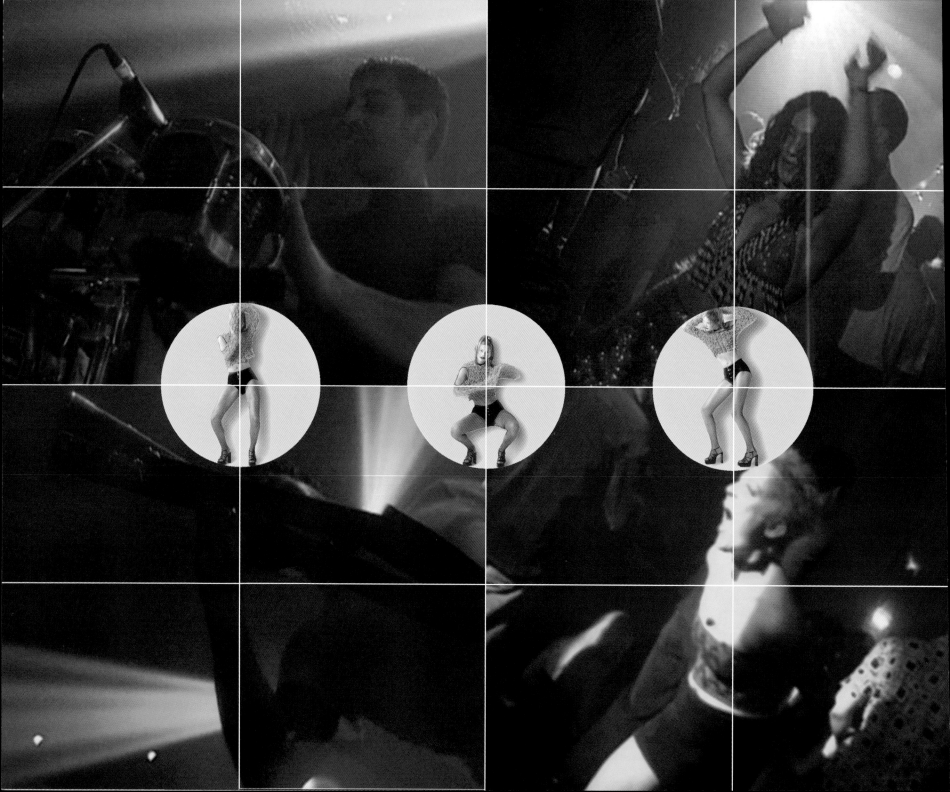

in the mix

in the mix

Weaving around behind his turntables and mixing desks, the DJ delivers two hundred beats per minute, creatively pasting together and transforming scraps of sound and music to put together tracks with a connective element. This is the DJ's world of mix 'n' match, remix and sampling.

Incorporating advanced sampling and scanning functionality, this outfit enables the DJ to step out from behind his turntables and move among the audience while continuing to shape the groove, thus ending the traditional separation between performer and audience. Similarly, electronic clubwear enables the audience to feed back to the DJ. In this way, using the outfit's wireless connectivity, the DJ and the audience can influence each other and their surroundings with light and sound.

in the mix

The DJ outfit incorporates a body area network into which modules are 'buttoned'

Soft, flat speakers are integrated into the collar, which can be raised

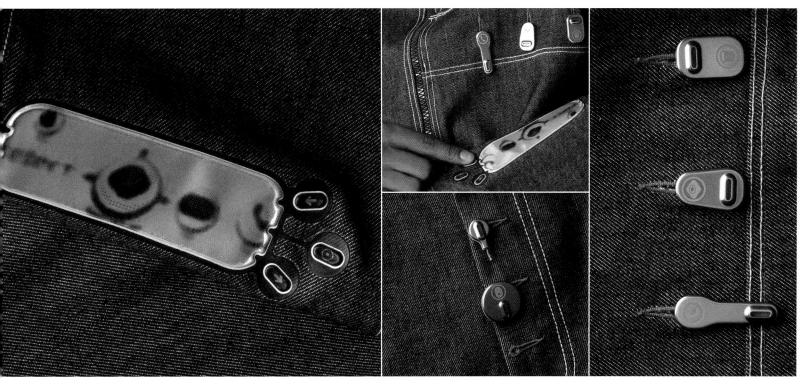

Flexible interface for control of audio functionality   Devices such as phone, audio and personal digital assistant are designed as fashion accessories

surround sound

surround sound

The audio jacket is an expressive item of streetwear for young people, providing personal downloadable sound entertainment on the move. The smart pocket has been designed specifically for a digital audio player, with an easy jack-plug connection to interface with the audio controls. A flash ram loader for audio memory has been integrated into the sleeve, and the flash ram cards can be loaded by opening a Velcro™ flap. In addition, headphones have been integrated into the hood of the jacket to create a totally immersive audio space. All these integrated audio devices can be controlled via a control panel on the sleeve for easy access, with a simple user interface for play, pause, forward, rewind and volume. On the back of the jacket there is an electroluminescent digital display serving as an embedded spectrum analyser, with the emitted light pulsating at the frequencies of the music being played.

surround sound

The audio jacket provides personal downloadable music on the move

The audio control panel is integrated in the sleeve for easy access

audio pocket with easy plug connection   Headphones integrated in the jacket hood create a totally immersive audio space   The display reacts to the sound frequency

close encounters

close encounters

Across the spectrum of social interaction, rapid access to knowledge about people, places and cultural nuances is becoming increasingly important. We have to meet the right people at the right time in the right place under the right circumstances, which means having to have the right information. This garment could be a useful tool to help us to make contact more easily wherever we are, whatever we're doing.

The jacket's small embedded camera records the wearer's environment. The system is then able to recognise the face of anyone encountered on a particular day. The integrated collar headphones provide audio feedback, discreetly reminding the wearer of the identity of the person just met and details of any previous encounters, whispering a transcript of a conversation in the wearer's ear or guiding him/her to an unfamiliar address. And, of course, the small lightweight camera can also capture special moments on holiday or other events, so that they can be shared with family and friends, e.g. via the Internet.

close encounters

The eyecam on the jacket has a face-recognition feature

The printed conductive interface controls are activated by sliding the eyecam up and dow

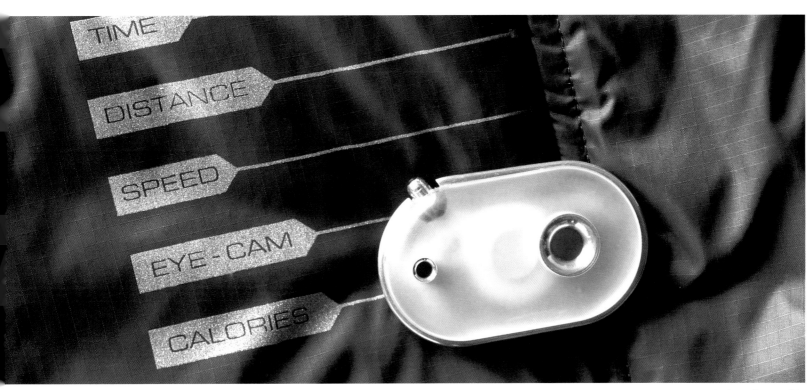

TIME

DISTANCE

SPEED

EYE-CAM

CALORIES

The jacket is reversible

embody

enhanced body care and adornment

feels good

124

feels good

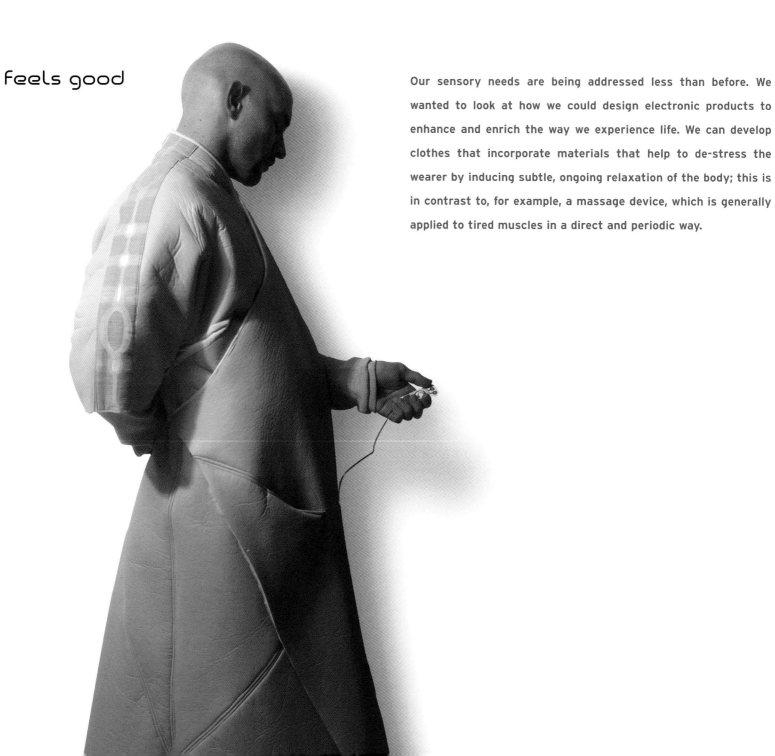

Our sensory needs are being addressed less than before. We wanted to look at how we could design electronic products to enhance and enrich the way we experience life. We can develop clothes that incorporate materials that help to de-stress the wearer by inducing subtle, ongoing relaxation of the body; this is in contrast to, for example, a massage device, which is generally applied to tired muscles in a direct and periodic way.

Advanced weaving of conductive threads combines tradition and technology for the enhanced well-being and comfort of the user. The cream kimono shown here has a conductive embroidered spine at the back, which is able to disperse an electrostatic charge via the fibres on the inside. This creates a tingling sensation that relaxes the wearer. Inside the pocket there is a remote device with a number of different settings for the various levels of relaxation. Biometric sensors monitor the degree of relaxation and adjust the level of sensory stimulation accordingly.

feels good

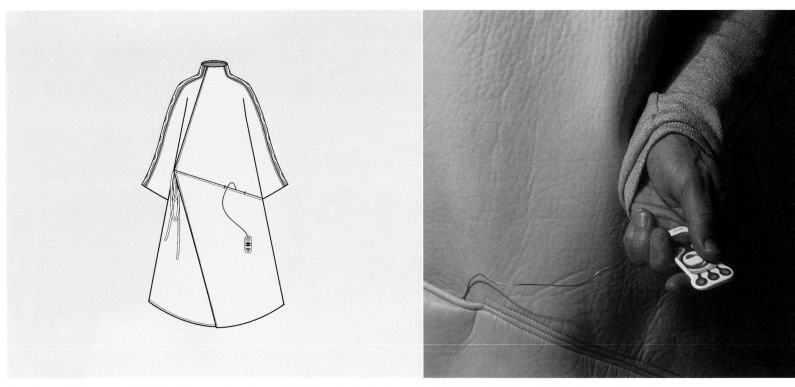

The weaving of conductive threads merges tradition and technology for enhanced well-being

The pocket remote activates various relaxation levels

The decorative pathways contain biometric sensors and woven conductive fibres

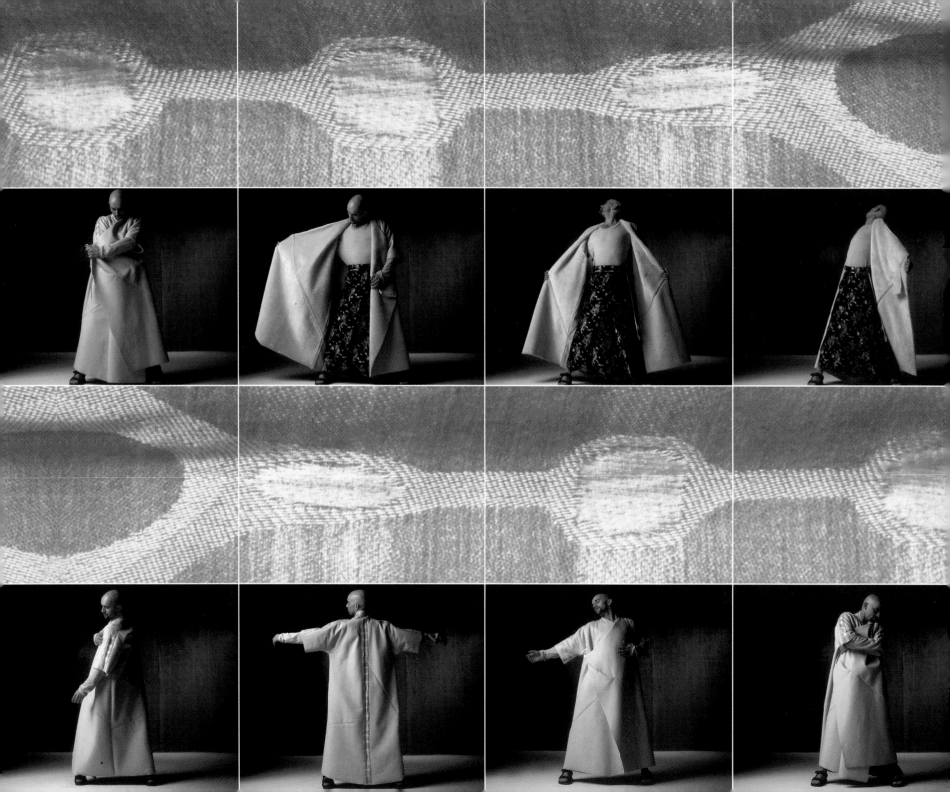

micro climate

micro climate

We live in a world where there are toxins in the air we breathe, in the food we eat, in the water we drink. Insecticides, pesticides and herbicides are sprayed all around us. There are already indications of a significant rise in allergy problems among children. In many major cities around the world, people are increasingly wearing masks to protect themselves against the unhealthy fumes from industry and traffic. Is this the street scene of the future?

With this garment, an electronic filter protects the wearer from, for instance, chemical pollutants while out and about in the city. At the same time he or she can receive regular information updates or enjoy music via the wireless clip-on audio device that links to the headphones integrated into the hood. The headphones have external controls for ease of use while the wearer is engaged in activity. The fabric contains an internal woven membrane that uses conductive yarns to connect interfaces.

micro climate

The microclimate jacket provides atmospheric protection and music on the move

Volume control

External control for ease of use   Solid-state audio device

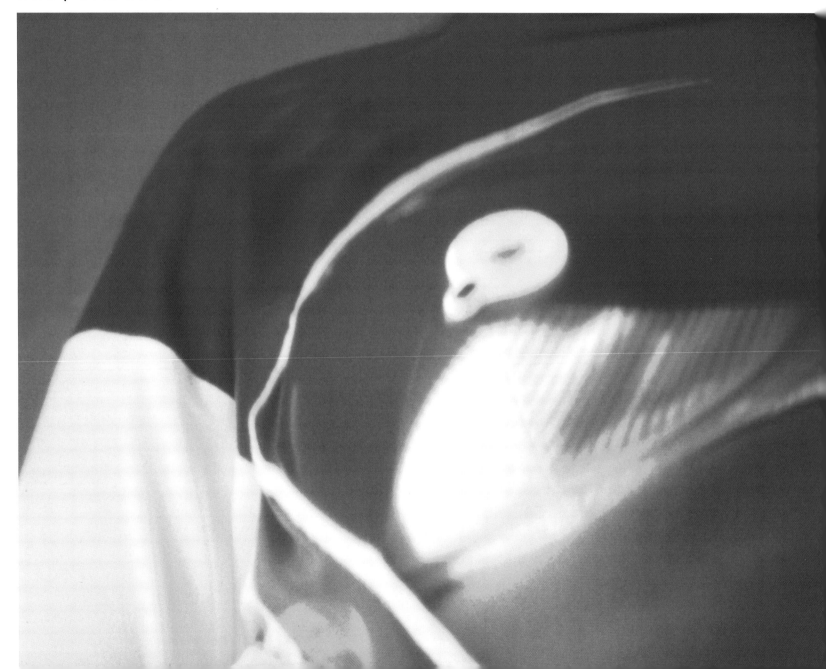

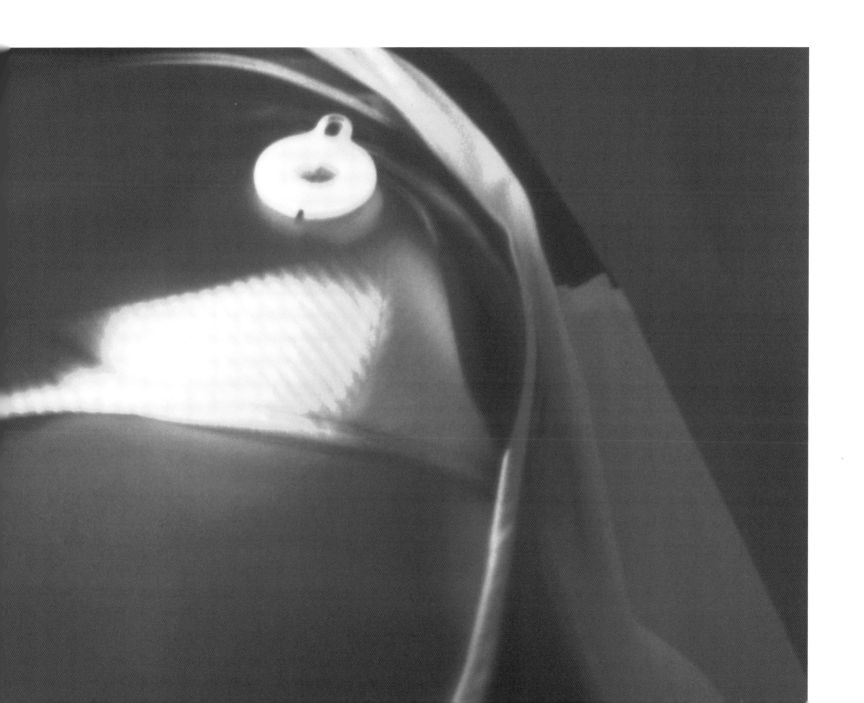

body and soul

Why, at the dawn of a new millennium, do we find that young people have resorted to the most 'primitive' forms of body adornment? For many, it is a way to break away from existing norms, from stereotypical behaviour, for others it is the result of contact with other cultures or simply another way to express their identity. Tattoos, body piercing, scarifications, pocketing and implants are as personal a statement as anyone can possibly make. While conventional society might tend to consider these as new and extreme forms of body adornment, an expressive medium used mainly by young people, they have existed for centuries in many different cultures as a traditional form of cultural or religious expression.

The integration of fashion and style into the human body is a precursor to a new medium that encompasses other functionalities: the body as a local area network. This theme has already been explored by institutions such as The Media Lab, and many research projects have examined the possibilities of harnessing human power. The passing of data through the body and sensing of biometric feedback have also been extensively covered. Medical biosensing, for example, could have extremely practical applications in the treatment of chronic and acute conditions, e.g. for reading insulin levels in the case of diabetes. Exploration into 'swallowables' that pass through the body or implants in the form of small electronic and mechanical devices has shown interesting potential. And though for many people this immediately raises the spectre of mankind being turned into a race of cyborgs, we should remember that we are in fact already using such devices on a fairly large scale for medical purposes (consider, for example, the pacemaker).

Today, on the threshold of a new era, the question facing companies operating at the interface of clothing and electronics is: How do we anticipate and develop clothing applications and solutions that address people's socio-cultural, emotional and physical needs, enabling them to express all the facets of their personality? Integrated technology clearly has a major role to play. Taking this exciting pioneering development to its ultimate, logical conclusion, the challenge facing us, in the end, is to extend the human nervous system to the seventh sense.

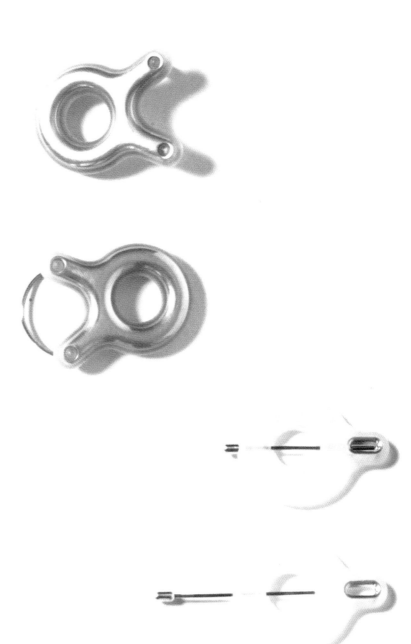

body and soul

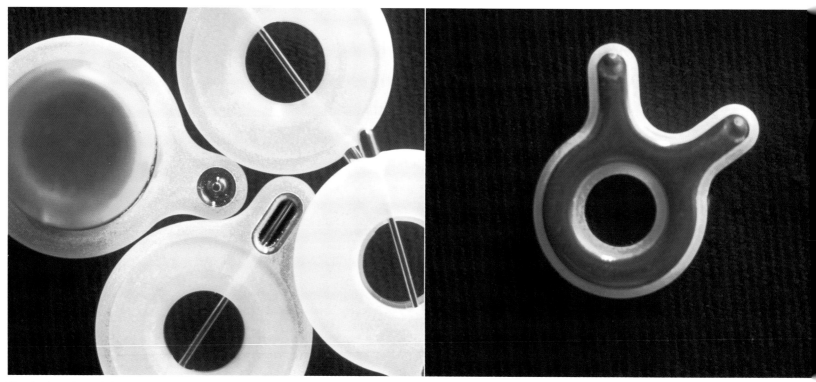

The piercings glow and give a pulsating sensation when the wearer is paged

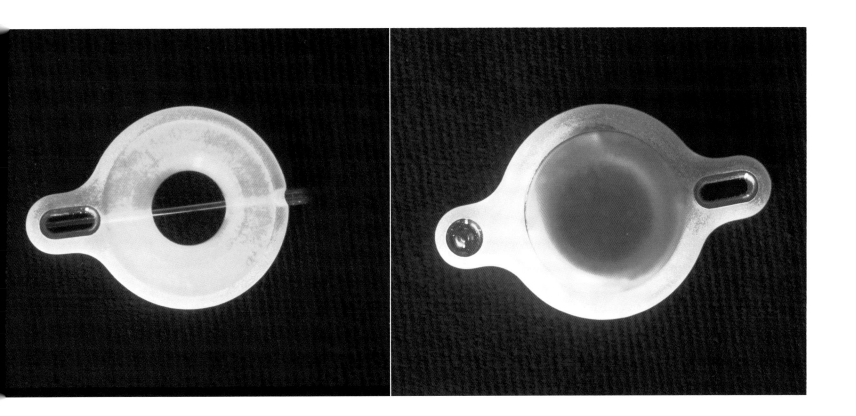

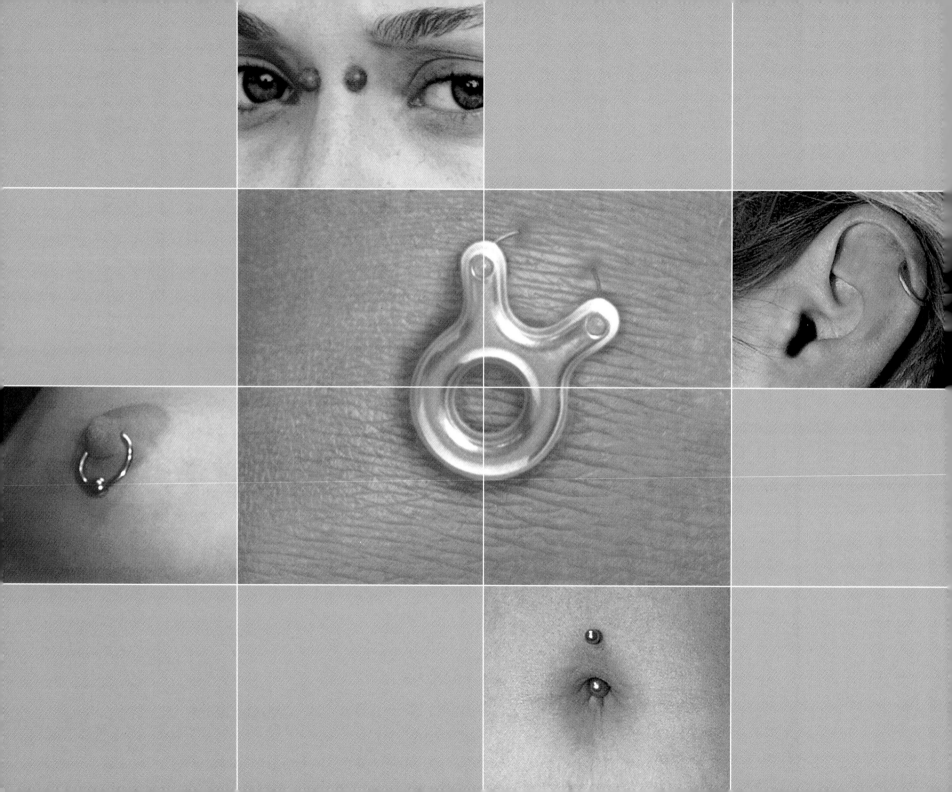

Acknowledgements

Wearables Strategic Direction

Stefano Marzano

Clive van Heerden

Philips Design Wearables Team

Project Management

Clive van Heerden

Linda Vodegel Matzen

Creative Direction

Jack Mama

Concept Development,

Apparel Design

Nancy Tilbury

Textile Design

Philippa Wagner

Project Coordination

Lesh Parameswaren

Apparel Production

Juliette Allen

James Church

Canan Geyik

Francis Geesin

Kiki Halfmeier

Sophie Jacobson

Alexie Sommer

Warren Valentine

Product Design,
Apparel Graphic Design

Roland Bird

Robert Green

Jack Mama

Sandra Nicholson

Bertrand Rigot

Nathan Sparshot

Martine Shepperd

Roger Swales

Paul Thursfield

Giang Vu

George Marmaropoulos

3D Visualisation

Paul Thursfield

Philips Research Wearables Team

Technical Project Leader

David Eves

Technical Direction

Paul Gough

Simon Turner

Engineering

Richard Cole

Jonny Farringdon

Asher Hoskins

Andrew Moore

Phil Neaves

Book Design

Project Coordination

Creative Direction, Graphic Design

Marion Verbucken, Philips Design

Editorial Team

David Eves

Josephine Green

Clive van Heerden

Jack Mama

Stefano Marzano

Laura Traldi

Marion Verbücken

Final Editing

Andrew Baxter Associates, Hilversum

Kenneth Gilbert, Philips Translation

Services, Eindhoven

Photography

Rens van Mierlo

Korff & van Mierlo, Eindhoven

Photo Assistant

Odette Geldens

Photo Coordination

Inge van Osch

Marjolein de Rooij

Lithography

Neroc Eindhoven B.V.

Printing

Roto Smeets Services

For more information contact:

Philips Research NL
Public Relations Philips Research
Prof. Holstlaan 4
5656 AA Eindhoven
www.research.philips.com
resinfo@philips.com
tel: +31 40 27 42321
fax: +31 40 27 44947

Philips Design NL
Media Relations Philips Design
Emmasingel 26, building HWD
5600 MD Eindhoven
The Netherlands
www.design.philips.com
press.design@philips.com
tel: +31 40 27 59115
fax: +31 40 27 59091

Philips Design USA
Intelligent Fibres
Holbrook House
345 Scarborough Road
Briarcliff Manor
New York 10510-2099 USA
clive.vanheerden@philips.com
tel: +1 (914) 945 6351
fax: +1 (914) 945 6399

With thanks to

Dance Salon Eindhoven

Bonnefanten Museum Maastricht

Schiphol Amsterdam

Olympia Fitnesswereld Eindhoven

Duty Station Managment of Canary Wharf,

North Greenwich, London Bridge